ENJOY ARITHMETIC!

John and Patricia Moore

PRACTICE EXAMPLES BASIC MULTIPLICATION

Book Three

POND VIEW
Otford

First published in Great Britain by
Hawthorns Publications Limited,
Pond View House, Otford, Kent.

Reprinted 1990, 1991, 1992, 1993, 1994, 1995

ISBN 1 871044 05 7

Printed in Great Britain by
Longmore Press Limited,
Park Lane, Otford, Sevenoaks,
Kent TN14 5PG.

FOREWORD

This is not a teaching scheme, but sets of exercises for the use of Primary School pupils, and pupils in Secondary Schools in need of revision in basic Arithmetic.

No attempt has been made to suggest methods for working. There is often more than one perfectly legitimate way of obtaining the correct answer. We do not believe that slower pupils should be confused by being confronted with a different method from the one used by their teacher. Very carefully graded material is used, with correct development of steps, introducing one difficulty at a time.

In the early material on Addition and Subtraction great emphasis has been placed on the number bond 10 ($1+9=10$, $2+8=10$, etc). This is included in almost every example.

In Subtraction, some children find it extremely difficult to subtract from 0. This may be laziness, but frequently they have had little grounding in "making up to 10". They need, therefore, much practice to cope with this particular difficulty. For this reason, we do not apologise for repetition in basic processes.

In the books dealing with Multiplication and Division digits have been repeated many times to reinforce learning the table. The table square is included inside the Multiplication front cover. It is always available for reference, if needed.

In Division by divisors up to 12 care has been taken to use the simplest carrying figures in the early stages, gradually increasing in difficulty by very easy steps. Long division has been included, although it is not now popular with many teachers, or included in many schemes. This, in our experience, can be taught with greater ease if the units digit is 1 in the divisor. It is easier to divide by 91 than by 19. The first stage, therefore, is division by 21, 31, 41, etc, and then increasing the units digit by easy stages to 22, 32, 42, etc, and 23, 33, 43, etc. It is also valuable to have the multiplication table of the divisor written out, and this we have asked the pupils to do. In our opinion, long division is worthy of more attention, as it gives practice in subtraction and multiplication, as well as division.

We have used large type, and would recommend that the examples be copied carefully by the pupils, preferably using squared books, so that —

a) the digits are spaced out adequately, and

b) the columns are quite distinct and straight.

Children who are not given prepared columns to work with initially are inclined to ignore the fact that columns are required, and squash all the numbers together.

How the book is used is left entirely to the discretion of the teacher, who knows the needs of particular individuals. Even in a small Remedial Unit there will be pupils of varying abilities, with very different weaknesses. Backward pupils need to have evidence of progress, even if it is slow. The work has to be arranged so that the end of an exercise is always in sight, and attainable.

In examples involving problems, the language used has been kept very simple, so that difficulties with reading will not hamper arithmetical attainment.

We hope that the very carefully graded exercises in these books will be to the mutual advantage of teachers and their pupils in the quest for high standards of numeracy.

John and Patricia Moore

CONTENTS

EXERCISE M1

1. 5 x 2	2. 4 x 2	3. 6 x 2	4. 7 x 2	5. 3 x 2
6. 3 x 3	7. 8 x 3	8. 5 x 3	9. 7 x 3	10. 4 x 3
11. 12 x 2	12. 8 x 2	13. 9 x 2	14. 10 x 2	15. 11 x 2
16. 6 x 3	17. 9 x 3	18. 10 x 3	19. 11 x 3	20. 12 x 3
21. 3 x 4	22. 4 x 4	23. 7 x 4	24. 5 x 4	25. 6 x 4

EXERCISE M2

1. 3 x 5	2. 7 x 5	3. 6 x 5	4. 5 x 5	5. 4 x 5
6. 8 x 4	7. 9 x 4	8. 2 x 4	9. 10 x 4	10. 12 x 4
11. 8 x 5	12. 9 x 5	13. 11 x 5	14. 10 x 5	15. 12 x 5
16. 7 x 6	17. 9 x 6	18. 5 x 6	19. 4 x 6	20. 3 x 6
21. 4 x 7	22. 3 x 7	23. 2 x 7	24. 5 x 7	25. 6 x 7

EXERCISE M3

1. 12 x 6	2. 11 x 6	3. 10 x 6	4. 6 x 6	5. 8 x 6
6. 8 x 7	7. 10 x 7	8. 9 x 7	9. 11 x 7	10. 12 x 7
11. 4 x 8	12. 3 x 8	13. 5 x 8	14. 6 x 8	15. 8 x 8
16. 5 x 9	17. 6 x 9	18. 2 x 9	19. 7 x 9	20. 3 x 9
21. 9 x 8	22. 7 x 8	23. 12 x 8	24. 11 x 8	25. 10 x 8

EXERCISE M4

1. 4 x 9	2. 8 x 9	3. 9 x 9	4. 11 x 9	5. 12 x 9
6. 5 x 10	7. 6 x 10	8. 8 x 10	9. 9 x 10	10. 4 x 10
11. 4 x 11	12. 3 x 11	13. 2 x 11	14. 6 x 11	15. 7 x 11
16. 7 x 10	17. 3 x 10	18. 10 x 10	19. 11 x 10	20. 12 x 10
21. 11 x 11	22. 10 x 11	23. 12 x 11	24. 9 x 11	25. 5 x 11

EXERCISE M5

1. 6 x 12	2. 7 x 12	3. 8 x 12	4. 4 x 12	5. 5 x 12
6. 11 x 12	7. 10 x 12	8. 12 x 12	9. 9 x 12	10. 3 x 12
11. 12 x 2	12. 13 x 2	13. 10 x 2	14. 14 x 2	15. 11 x 2
16. 23 x 2	17. 20 x 2	18. 24 x 2	19. 22 x 2	20. 21 x 2
21. 33 x 2	22. 31 x 2	23. 34 x 2	24. 30 x 2	25. 32 x 2

EXERCISE M6

1. 43 x 2	2. 44 x 2	3. 42 x 2	4. 41 x 2	5. 40 x 2
6. 51 x 2	7. 54 x 2	8. 52 x 2	9. 50 x 2	10. 53 x 2
11. 15 x 2	12. 16 x 2	13. 17 x 2	14. 18 x 2	15. 19 x 2
16. 25 x 2	17. 28 x 2	18. 26 x 2	19. 27 x 2	20. 29 x 2
21. 39 x 2	22. 38 x 2	23. 36 x 2	24. 35 x 2	25. 37 x 2

EXERCISE M7

1. 48 × 2	2. 47 × 2	3. 45 × 2	4. 46 × 2	5. 49 × 2
6. 56 × 2	7. 57 × 2	8. 58 × 2	9. 59 × 2	10. 55 × 2
11. 67 × 2	12. 66 × 2	13. 68 × 2	14. 69 × 2	15. 65 × 2
16. 14 × 3	17. 16 × 3	18. 17 × 3	19. 18 × 3	20. 19 × 3
21. 14 × 4	22. 17 × 4	23. 19 × 4	24. 18 × 4	25. 16 × 4

EXERCISE M8

1. 14 x 5	2. 19 x 5	3. 16 x 5	4. 17 x 5	5. 18 x 5
6. 19 x 6	7. 16 x 6	8. 14 x 6	9. 15 x 6	10. 17 x 6
11. 13 x 7	12. 14 x 7	13. 17 x 7	14. 15 x 7	15. 19 x 7
16. 13 x 8	17. 19 x 8	18. 17 x 8	19. 16 x 8	20. 14 x 8
21. 13 x 9	22. 15 x 9	23. 16 x 9	24. 18 x 9	25. 17 x 9

EXERCISE M9

1. 24 x 3	2. 26 x 3	3. 27 x 3	4. 28 x 3	5. 29 x 3
6. 25 x 3	7. 22 x 3	8. 27 x 4	9. 26 x 4	10. 25 x 4
11. 28 x 4	12. 29 x 4	13. 26 x 5	14. 28 x 5	15. 29 x 5
16. 25 x 5	17. 27 x 6	18. 28 x 6	19. 29 x 6	20. 26 x 6
21. 25 x 6	22. 28 x 7	23. 29 x 7	24. 27 x 7	25. 25 x 7

EXERCISE M10

1. 26 × 7	2. 26 × 8	3. 27 × 8	4. 28 × 8	5. 29 × 8
6. 24 × 8	7. 24 × 9	8. 26 × 9	9. 28 × 9	10. 29 × 9
11. 27 × 9	12. 34 × 3	13. 35 × 3	14. 36 × 3	15. 37 × 3
16. 38 × 3	17. 35 × 4	18. 36 × 4	19. 37 × 4	20. 39 × 4
21. 34 × 4	22. 39 × 5	23. 35 × 5	24. 36 × 5	25. 38 × 5

EXERCISE M11

1. 37 x 6	2. 38 x 6	3. 36 x 6	4. 35 x 6	5. 39 x 6
6. 38 x 7	7. 36 x 7	8. 35 x 7	9. 39 x 7	10. 37 x 7
11. 36 x 8	12. 35 x 8	13. 37 x 8	14. 38 x 8	15. 39 x 8
16. 37 x 9	17. 36 x 9	18. 39 x 9	19. 35 x 9	20. 38 x 9
21. 44 x 3	22. 45 x 3	23. 46 x 3	24. 47 x 3	25. 48 x 3

EXERCISE M12

1. 45 x 4 ____	2. 48 x 4 ____	3. 49 x 4 ____	4. 46 x 4 ____	5. 47 x 4 ____
6. 47 x 5 ____	7. 46 x 5 ____	8. 48 x 5 ____	9. 49 x 5 ____	10. 45 x 5 ____
11. 48 x 6 ____	12. 47 x 6 ____	13. 46 x 6 ____	14. 49 x 6 ____	15. 45 x 6 ____
16. 49 x 7 ____	17. 46 x 7 ____	18. 48 x 7 ____	19. 47 x 7 ____	20. 45 x 7 ____
21. 46 x 8 ____	22. 45 x 8 ____	23. 47 x 8 ____	24. 49 x 8 ____	25. 48 x 8 ____

EXERCISE M13

1. 49 x 9	2. 46 x 9	3. 47 x 9	4. 48 x 9	5. 45 x 9
6. 56 x 3	7. 57 x 3	8. 59 x 3	9. 58 x 3	10. 54 x 3
11. 57 x 4	12. 56 x 4	13. 58 x 4	14. 59 x 4	15. 54 x 4
16. 56 x 5	17. 57 x 5	18. 58 x 5	19. 59 x 5	20. 55 x 5
21. 57 x 6	22. 56 x 6	23. 58 x 6	24. 59 x 6	25. 54 x 6

EXERCISE M14

1. 56 x 7	2. 58 x 7	3. 59 x 7	4. 55 x 7	5. 57 x 7
6. 58 x 8	7. 56 x 8	8. 57 x 8	9. 59 x 8	10. 55 x 8
11. 59 x 9	12. 56 x 9	13. 57 x 9	14. 58 x 9	15. 54 x 9
16. 64 x 3	17. 65 x 3	18. 67 x 3	19. 68 x 3	20. 69 x 3
21. 63 x 4	22. 62 x 4	23. 65 x 4	24. 66 x 4	25. 67 x 4

EXERCISE M15

1. 66 x 5	2. 67 x 5	3. 68 x 5	4. 64 x 5	5. 65 x 5
6. 63 x 6	7. 67 x 6	8. 64 x 6	9. 68 x 6	10. 65 x 6
11. 68 x 7	12. 62 x 7	13. 63 x 7	14. 64 x 7	15. 68 x 7
16. 69 x 8	17. 64 x 8	18. 63 x 8	19. 68 x 8	20. 67 x 8
21. 64 x 9	22. 65 x 9	23. 67 x 9	24. 68 x 9	25. 69 x 9

EXERCISE M16

1. 74 x 3	2. 76 x 3	3. 78 x 3	4. 79 x 3	5. 75 x 3
6. 74 x 4	7. 76 x 4	8. 78 x 4	9. 73 x 4	10. 76 x 4
11. 76 x 5	12. 73 x 5	13. 74 x 5	14. 78 x 5	15. 79 x 5
16. 72 x 6	17. 73 x 6	18. 74 x 6	19. 75 x 6	20. 76 x 6
21. 74 x 7	22. 73 x 7	23. 72 x 7	24. 78 x 7	25. 76 x 7

EXERCISE M17

1. 78 x 8	2. 76 x 8	3. 72 x 8	4. 73 x 8	5. 74 x 8
6. 79 x 9	7. 74 x 9	8. 73 x 9	9. 76 x 9	10. 78 x 9
11. 83 x 3	12. 86 x 3	13. 84 x 3	14. 87 x 3	15. 85 x 3
16. 82 x 4	17. 86 x 4	18. 87 x 4	19. 84 x 4	20. 85 x 4
21. 86 x 5	22. 87 x 5	23. 88 x 5	24. 89 x 5	25. 82 x 5

EXERCISE M18

1. 87 x 6	2. 86 x 6	3. 84 x 6	4. 85 x 6	5. 89 x 6
6. 86 x 7	7. 84 x 7	8. 82 x 7	9. 83 x 7	10. 86 x 7
11. 89 x 8	12. 83 x 8	13. 86 x 8	14. 87 x 8	15. 84 x 8
16. 86 x 9	17. 84 x 9	18. 82 x 9	19. 83 x 9	20. 88 x 9
21. 92 x 3	22. 94 x 3	23. 96 x 3	24. 95 x 3	25. 98 x 3

EXERCISE M19

1. 96 x 4	2. 93 x 4	3. 95 x 4	4. 98 x 4	5. 94 x 4
6. 97 x 5	7. 96 x 5	8. 93 x 5	9. 94 x 5	10. 98 x 5
11. 96 x 6	12. 92 x 6	13. 94 x 6	14. 95 x 6	15. 98 x 6
16. 98 x 7	17. 93 x 7	18. 94 x 7	19. 98 x 7	20. 97 x 7
21. 96 x 8	22. 97 x 8	23. 95 x 8	24. 94 x 8	25. 93 x 8

EXERCISE M20

1. 146 x 2	2. 157 x 2	3. 169 x 2	4. 186 x 2
5. 276 x 2	6. 259 x 2	7. 289 x 2	8. 298 x 2
9. 148 x 3	10. 156 x 3	11. 167 x 3	12. 186 x 3
13. 269 x 3	14. 282 x 3	15. 257 x 3	16. 269 x 3
17. 157 x 4	18. 158 x 4	19. 178 x 4	20. 199 x 4

EXERCISE M21

1. 298 x 4
2. 274 x 4
3. 289 x 4
4. 274 x 4
5. 143 x 5
6. 149 x 5
7. 156 x 5
8. 169 x 5
9. 264 x 5
10. 293 x 5
11. 286 x 5
12. 278 x 5
13. 198 x 6
14. 164 x 6
15. 137 x 6
16. 158 x 6
17. 168 x 6
18. 274 x 6
19. 285 x 6
20. 297 x 6

EXERCISE M22

1. 179 x 7	2. 186 x 7	3. 195 x 7	4. 136 x 7
5. 299 x 7	6. 266 x 7	7. 279 x 7	8. 256 x 7
9. 184 x 8	10. 193 x 8	11. 146 x 8	12. 159 x 8
13. 296 x 8	14. 265 x 8	15. 286 x 8	16. 294 x 8
17. 186 x 9	18. 164 x 9	19. 187 x 9	20. 165 x 9

EXERCISE M23

1. 276 x 9	2. 265 x 9	3. 259 x 9	4. 269 x 9
5. 106 x 2	6. 208 x 3	7. 309 x 4	8. 407 x 5
9. 504 x 6	10. 607 x 3	11. 702 x 8	12. 801 x 9
13. 140 x 2	14. 260 x 3	15. 350 x 4	16. 470 x 5
17. 590 x 6	18. 630 x 7	19. 720 x 8	20. 810 x 9

EXERCISE M24

1. 14 x10	2. 17 x10	3. 18 x10	4. 19 x10
5. 21 x10	6. 26 x10	7. 28 x10	8. 29 x10
9. 32 x10	10. 35 x10	11. 36 x10	12. 38 x10
13. 46 x10	14. 57 x10	15. 63 x10	16. 67 x10
17. 72 x10	18. 84 x10	19. 96 x10	20. 99 x10

EXERCISE M25

1. 100 x 10	2. 109 x 10	3. 116 x 10	4. 129 x 10
5. 146 x 10	6. 153 x 10	7. 179 x 10	8. 268 x 10
9. 279 x 10	10. 386 x 10	11. 398 x 10	12. 400 x 10
13. 465 x 10	14. 478 x 10	15. 486 x 10	16. 500 x 10
17. 565 x 10	18. 600 x 10	19. 604 x 10	20. 650 x 10

EXERCISE M26

1. $\begin{array}{r} 16 \\ \times 11 \\ \hline \end{array}$	2. $\begin{array}{r} 19 \\ \times 11 \\ \hline \end{array}$	3. $\begin{array}{r} 20 \\ \times 11 \\ \hline \end{array}$	4. $\begin{array}{r} 23 \\ \times 11 \\ \hline \end{array}$
5. $\begin{array}{r} 26 \\ \times 11 \\ \hline \end{array}$	6. $\begin{array}{r} 30 \\ \times 11 \\ \hline \end{array}$	7. $\begin{array}{r} 35 \\ \times 11 \\ \hline \end{array}$	8. $\begin{array}{r} 37 \\ \times 11 \\ \hline \end{array}$
9. $\begin{array}{r} 48 \\ \times 11 \\ \hline \end{array}$	10. $\begin{array}{r} 50 \\ \times 11 \\ \hline \end{array}$	11. $\begin{array}{r} 52 \\ \times 11 \\ \hline \end{array}$	12. $\begin{array}{r} 65 \\ \times 11 \\ \hline \end{array}$
13. $\begin{array}{r} 70 \\ \times 11 \\ \hline \end{array}$	14. $\begin{array}{r} 76 \\ \times 11 \\ \hline \end{array}$	15. $\begin{array}{r} 78 \\ \times 11 \\ \hline \end{array}$	16. $\begin{array}{r} 80 \\ \times 11 \\ \hline \end{array}$
17. $\begin{array}{r} 86 \\ \times 11 \\ \hline \end{array}$	18. $\begin{array}{r} 90 \\ \times 11 \\ \hline \end{array}$	19. $\begin{array}{r} 95 \\ \times 11 \\ \hline \end{array}$	20. $\begin{array}{r} 99 \\ \times 11 \\ \hline \end{array}$

EXERCISE M27

1. 100 x11	2. 108 x11	3. 116 x11	4. 120 x11
5. 126 x11	6. 130 x11	7. 132 x11	8. 140 x11
9. 146 x11	10. 150 x11	11. 156 x11	12. 159 x11
13. 161 x11	14. 169 x11	15. 170 x11	16. 209 x11
17. 310 x11	18. 461 x11	19. 560 x11	20. 660 x11

EXERCISE M28

1. 606 x 11 ____	2. 780 x 11 ____	3. 701 x 11 ____	4. 765 x 11 ____
5. 786 x 11 ____	6. 800 x 11 ____	7. 806 x 11 ____	8. 819 x 11 ____
9. 820 x 11 ____	10. 835 x 11 ____	11. 850 x 11 ____	12. 856 x 11 ____
13. 860 x 11 ____	14. 876 x 11 ____	15. 880 x 11 ____	16. 900 x 11 ____
17. 970 x 11 ____	18. 984 x 11 ____	19. 996 x 11 ____	20. 999 x 11 ____

EXERCISE M29

1. $\begin{array}{r} 10 \\ \times 12 \\ \hline \end{array}$	2. $\begin{array}{r} 11 \\ \times 12 \\ \hline \end{array}$	3. $\begin{array}{r} 12 \\ \times 12 \\ \hline \end{array}$	4. $\begin{array}{r} 13 \\ \times 12 \\ \hline \end{array}$
5. $\begin{array}{r} 15 \\ \times 12 \\ \hline \end{array}$	6. $\begin{array}{r} 16 \\ \times 12 \\ \hline \end{array}$	7. $\begin{array}{r} 17 \\ \times 12 \\ \hline \end{array}$	8. $\begin{array}{r} 18 \\ \times 12 \\ \hline \end{array}$
9. $\begin{array}{r} 19 \\ \times 12 \\ \hline \end{array}$	10. $\begin{array}{r} 20 \\ \times 12 \\ \hline \end{array}$	11. $\begin{array}{r} 21 \\ \times 12 \\ \hline \end{array}$	12. $\begin{array}{r} 23 \\ \times 12 \\ \hline \end{array}$
13. $\begin{array}{r} 25 \\ \times 12 \\ \hline \end{array}$	14. $\begin{array}{r} 27 \\ \times 12 \\ \hline \end{array}$	15. $\begin{array}{r} 29 \\ \times 12 \\ \hline \end{array}$	16. $\begin{array}{r} 30 \\ \times 12 \\ \hline \end{array}$
17. $\begin{array}{r} 32 \\ \times 12 \\ \hline \end{array}$	18. $\begin{array}{r} 34 \\ \times 12 \\ \hline \end{array}$	19. $\begin{array}{r} 36 \\ \times 12 \\ \hline \end{array}$	20. $\begin{array}{r} 38 \\ \times 12 \\ \hline \end{array}$

EXERCISE M30

1. $\begin{array}{r} 41 \\ \times 12 \\ \hline \\ \hline \end{array}$	2. $\begin{array}{r} 43 \\ \times 12 \\ \hline \\ \hline \end{array}$	3. $\begin{array}{r} 45 \\ \times 12 \\ \hline \\ \hline \end{array}$	4. $\begin{array}{r} 47 \\ \times 12 \\ \hline \\ \hline \end{array}$
5. $\begin{array}{r} 49 \\ \times 12 \\ \hline \\ \hline \end{array}$	6. $\begin{array}{r} 50 \\ \times 12 \\ \hline \\ \hline \end{array}$	7. $\begin{array}{r} 52 \\ \times 12 \\ \hline \\ \hline \end{array}$	8. $\begin{array}{r} 54 \\ \times 12 \\ \hline \\ \hline \end{array}$
9. $\begin{array}{r} 56 \\ \times 12 \\ \hline \\ \hline \end{array}$	10. $\begin{array}{r} 58 \\ \times 12 \\ \hline \\ \hline \end{array}$	11. $\begin{array}{r} 61 \\ \times 12 \\ \hline \\ \hline \end{array}$	12. $\begin{array}{r} 63 \\ \times 12 \\ \hline \\ \hline \end{array}$
13. $\begin{array}{r} 65 \\ \times 12 \\ \hline \\ \hline \end{array}$	14. $\begin{array}{r} 67 \\ \times 12 \\ \hline \\ \hline \end{array}$	15. $\begin{array}{r} 69 \\ \times 12 \\ \hline \\ \hline \end{array}$	16. $\begin{array}{r} 70 \\ \times 12 \\ \hline \\ \hline \end{array}$
17. $\begin{array}{r} 72 \\ \times 12 \\ \hline \\ \hline \end{array}$	18. $\begin{array}{r} 74 \\ \times 12 \\ \hline \\ \hline \end{array}$	19. $\begin{array}{r} 76 \\ \times 12 \\ \hline \\ \hline \end{array}$	20. $\begin{array}{r} 78 \\ \times 12 \\ \hline \\ \hline \end{array}$

EXERCISE M31

1. 81 x 12	2. 83 x 12	3. 85 x 12	4. 87 x 12
5. 89 x 12	6. 82 x 12	7. 84 x 12	8. 86 x 12
9. 88 x 12	10. 80 x 12	11. 91 x 12	12. 93 x 12
13. 95 x 12	14. 97 x 12	15. 99 x 12	16. 92 x 12
17. 94 x 12	18. 96 x 12	19. 98 x 12	20. 90 x 12

EXERCISE M32

1. 11 x 13	2. 13 x 13	3. 15 x 13	4. 17 x 13
5. 19 x 13	6. 12 x 13	7. 14 x 13	8. 16 x 13
9. 18 x 13	10. 20 x 13	11. 11 x 14	12. 13 x 14
13. 15 x 14	14. 17 x 14	15. 19 x 14	16. 12 x 14
17. 14 x 14	18. 16 x 14	19. 18 x 14	20. 20 x 14

EXERCISE M33

1. 11 x 15	2. 13 x 15	3. 15 x 15	4. 17 x 15
5. 19 x 15	6. 12 x 15	7. 14 x 15	8. 16 x 15
9. 18 x 15	10. 20 x 15	11. 11 x 16	12. 13 x 16
13. 15 x 16	14. 17 x 16	15. 19 x 16	16. 12 x 16
17. 14 x 16	18. 16 x 16	19. 18 x 16	20. 20 x 16

EXERCISE M34

1. 11 x 17	2. 13 x 17	3. 15 x 17	4. 17 x 17
5. 19 x 17	6. 12 x 17	7. 14 x 17	8. 16 x 17
9. 18 x 17	10. 20 x 17	11. 11 x 18	12. 13 x 18
13. 15 x 18	14. 17 x 18	15. 19 x 18	16. 12 x 18
17. 14 x 18	18. 16 x 18	19. 18 x 18	20. 20 x 18

EXERCISE M35

1. $\begin{array}{r} 11 \\ \times 19 \\ \hline \end{array}$	2. $\begin{array}{r} 13 \\ \times 19 \\ \hline \end{array}$	3. $\begin{array}{r} 15 \\ \times 19 \\ \hline \end{array}$	4. $\begin{array}{r} 17 \\ \times 19 \\ \hline \end{array}$
5. $\begin{array}{r} 19 \\ \times 19 \\ \hline \end{array}$	6. $\begin{array}{r} 12 \\ \times 19 \\ \hline \end{array}$	7. $\begin{array}{r} 14 \\ \times 19 \\ \hline \end{array}$	8. $\begin{array}{r} 16 \\ \times 19 \\ \hline \end{array}$
9. $\begin{array}{r} 18 \\ \times 19 \\ \hline \end{array}$	10. $\begin{array}{r} 20 \\ \times 19 \\ \hline \end{array}$	11. $\begin{array}{r} 11 \\ \times 20 \\ \hline \end{array}$	12. $\begin{array}{r} 13 \\ \times 20 \\ \hline \end{array}$
13. $\begin{array}{r} 15 \\ \times 20 \\ \hline \end{array}$	14. $\begin{array}{r} 17 \\ \times 20 \\ \hline \end{array}$	15. $\begin{array}{r} 19 \\ \times 20 \\ \hline \end{array}$	16. $\begin{array}{r} 12 \\ \times 20 \\ \hline \end{array}$
17. $\begin{array}{r} 14 \\ \times 20 \\ \hline \end{array}$	18. $\begin{array}{r} 16 \\ \times 20 \\ \hline \end{array}$	19. $\begin{array}{r} 18 \\ \times 20 \\ \hline \end{array}$	20. $\begin{array}{r} 20 \\ \times 20 \\ \hline \end{array}$

EXERCISE M36

1. $\begin{array}{r} 11 \\ \times 21 \\ \hline \end{array}$

2. $\begin{array}{r} 13 \\ \times 21 \\ \hline \end{array}$

3. $\begin{array}{r} 15 \\ \times 21 \\ \hline \end{array}$

4. $\begin{array}{r} 17 \\ \times 21 \\ \hline \end{array}$

5. $\begin{array}{r} 19 \\ \times 21 \\ \hline \end{array}$

6. $\begin{array}{r} 12 \\ \times 21 \\ \hline \end{array}$

7. $\begin{array}{r} 14 \\ \times 21 \\ \hline \end{array}$

8. $\begin{array}{r} 16 \\ \times 21 \\ \hline \end{array}$

9. $\begin{array}{r} 18 \\ \times 21 \\ \hline \end{array}$

10. $\begin{array}{r} 20 \\ \times 21 \\ \hline \end{array}$

11. $\begin{array}{r} 11 \\ \times 22 \\ \hline \end{array}$

12. $\begin{array}{r} 13 \\ \times 22 \\ \hline \end{array}$

13. $\begin{array}{r} 15 \\ \times 22 \\ \hline \end{array}$

14. $\begin{array}{r} 17 \\ \times 22 \\ \hline \end{array}$

15. $\begin{array}{r} 19 \\ \times 22 \\ \hline \end{array}$

16. $\begin{array}{r} 12 \\ \times 22 \\ \hline \end{array}$

17. $\begin{array}{r} 14 \\ \times 22 \\ \hline \end{array}$

18. $\begin{array}{r} 16 \\ \times 22 \\ \hline \end{array}$

19. $\begin{array}{r} 18 \\ \times 22 \\ \hline \end{array}$

20. $\begin{array}{r} 20 \\ \times 22 \\ \hline \end{array}$

EXERCISE M37

1. 11 x23	2. 13 x23	3. 15 x23	4. 17 x23
5. 19 x23	6. 12 x23	7. 14 x23	8. 16 x23
9. 18 x23	10. 20 x23	11. 11 x24	12. 13 x24
13. 15 x24	14. 17 x24	15. 19 x24	16. 12 x24
17. 14 x24	18. 16 x24	19. 18 x24	20. 20 x24

EXERCISE M38

1. $\begin{array}{r} 11 \\ \times 25 \\ \hline \end{array}$	2. $\begin{array}{r} 13 \\ \times 25 \\ \hline \end{array}$	3. $\begin{array}{r} 15 \\ \times 25 \\ \hline \end{array}$	4. $\begin{array}{r} 17 \\ \times 25 \\ \hline \end{array}$
5. $\begin{array}{r} 19 \\ \times 25 \\ \hline \end{array}$	6. $\begin{array}{r} 12 \\ \times 25 \\ \hline \end{array}$	7. $\begin{array}{r} 14 \\ \times 25 \\ \hline \end{array}$	8. $\begin{array}{r} 16 \\ \times 25 \\ \hline \end{array}$
9. $\begin{array}{r} 18 \\ \times 25 \\ \hline \end{array}$	10. $\begin{array}{r} 20 \\ \times 25 \\ \hline \end{array}$	11. $\begin{array}{r} 11 \\ \times 26 \\ \hline \end{array}$	12. $\begin{array}{r} 13 \\ \times 26 \\ \hline \end{array}$
13. $\begin{array}{r} 15 \\ \times 26 \\ \hline \\ \hline \end{array}$	14. $\begin{array}{r} 17 \\ \times 26 \\ \hline \\ \hline \end{array}$	15. $\begin{array}{r} 19 \\ \times 26 \\ \hline \\ \hline \end{array}$	16. $\begin{array}{r} 12 \\ \times 26 \\ \hline \\ \hline \end{array}$
17. $\begin{array}{r} 14 \\ \times 26 \\ \hline \end{array}$	18. $\begin{array}{r} 16 \\ \times 26 \\ \hline \end{array}$	19. $\begin{array}{r} 18 \\ \times 26 \\ \hline \end{array}$	20. $\begin{array}{r} 20 \\ \times 26 \\ \hline \end{array}$

EXERCISE M39

1. $\begin{array}{r} 11 \\ \times 27 \\ \hline \end{array}$	2. $\begin{array}{r} 13 \\ \times 27 \\ \hline \end{array}$	3. $\begin{array}{r} 17 \\ \times 27 \\ \hline \end{array}$	4. $\begin{array}{r} 19 \\ \times 27 \\ \hline \end{array}$
5. $\begin{array}{r} 14 \\ \times 27 \\ \hline \end{array}$	6. $\begin{array}{r} 16 \\ \times 27 \\ \hline \end{array}$	7. $\begin{array}{r} 18 \\ \times 27 \\ \hline \end{array}$	8. $\begin{array}{r} 13 \\ \times 28 \\ \hline \end{array}$
9. $\begin{array}{r} 15 \\ \times 28 \\ \hline \end{array}$	10. $\begin{array}{r} 17 \\ \times 28 \\ \hline \end{array}$	11. $\begin{array}{r} 19 \\ \times 28 \\ \hline \end{array}$	12. $\begin{array}{r} 12 \\ \times 28 \\ \hline \end{array}$
13. $\begin{array}{r} 14 \\ \times 28 \\ \hline \end{array}$	14. $\begin{array}{r} 20 \\ \times 28 \\ \hline \end{array}$	15. $\begin{array}{r} 13 \\ \times 29 \\ \hline \end{array}$	16. $\begin{array}{r} 15 \\ \times 29 \\ \hline \end{array}$
17. $\begin{array}{r} 19 \\ \times 29 \\ \hline \end{array}$	18. $\begin{array}{r} 12 \\ \times 29 \\ \hline \end{array}$	19. $\begin{array}{r} 16 \\ \times 29 \\ \hline \end{array}$	20. $\begin{array}{r} 18 \\ \times 29 \\ \hline \end{array}$

EXERCISE M40

1. 21 x 26	2. 23 x 26	3. 25 x 26	4. 27 x 26
5. 29 x 26	6. 22 x 26	7. 24 x 26	8. 26 x 26
9. 28 x 26	10. 30 x 26	11. 31 x 26	12. 33 x 26
13. 35 x 26	14. 37 x 26	15. 39 x 26	16. 32 x 26
17. 34 x 26	18. 36 x 26	19. 38 x 26	20. 40 x 26

EXERCISE M41

1. $\begin{array}{r} 41 \\ \times 26 \\ \hline \end{array}$	2. $\begin{array}{r} 43 \\ \times 26 \\ \hline \end{array}$	3. $\begin{array}{r} 45 \\ \times 26 \\ \hline \end{array}$	4. $\begin{array}{r} 47 \\ \times 26 \\ \hline \end{array}$
5. $\begin{array}{r} 49 \\ \times 26 \\ \hline \end{array}$	6. $\begin{array}{r} 42 \\ \times 26 \\ \hline \end{array}$	7. $\begin{array}{r} 44 \\ \times 26 \\ \hline \end{array}$	8. $\begin{array}{r} 46 \\ \times 26 \\ \hline \end{array}$
9. $\begin{array}{r} 48 \\ \times 26 \\ \hline \end{array}$	10. $\begin{array}{r} 50 \\ \times 26 \\ \hline \end{array}$	11. $\begin{array}{r} 51 \\ \times 26 \\ \hline \end{array}$	12. $\begin{array}{r} 53 \\ \times 26 \\ \hline \end{array}$
13. $\begin{array}{r} 55 \\ \times 26 \\ \hline \end{array}$	14. $\begin{array}{r} 57 \\ \times 26 \\ \hline \end{array}$	15. $\begin{array}{r} 59 \\ \times 26 \\ \hline \end{array}$	16. $\begin{array}{r} 52 \\ \times 26 \\ \hline \end{array}$
17. $\begin{array}{r} 54 \\ \times 26 \\ \hline \end{array}$	18. $\begin{array}{r} 56 \\ \times 26 \\ \hline \end{array}$	19. $\begin{array}{r} 58 \\ \times 26 \\ \hline \end{array}$	20. $\begin{array}{r} 60 \\ \times 26 \\ \hline \end{array}$

EXERCISE M42

1. 61 x 26	2. 63 x 26	3. 65 x 26	4. 67 x 26
5. 69 x 26	6. 62 x 26	7. 64 x 26	8. 66 x 26
9. 68 x 26	10. 70 x 26	11. 71 x 26	12. 73 x 26
13. 75 x 26	14. 77 x 26	15. 79 x 26	16. 72 x 26
17. 74 x 26	18. 76 x 26	19. 7.8 x 26	20. 8.0 x 26

EXERCISE M43

1. 81×26

2. 83×26

3. 85×26

4. 87×26

5. 89×26

6. 82×26

7. 84×26

8. 86×26

9. 88×26

10. 90×26

11. 91×26

12. 93×26

13. 95×26

14. 97×26

15. 99×26

16. 92×26

17. 94×26

18. 96×26

19. 98×26

20. 100×26

EXERCISE M44

1. 21 x 37	2. 23 x 37	3. 25 x 37	4. 27 x 37
5. 29 x 37	6. 22 x 37	7. 24 x 37	8. 26 x 37
9. 28 x 37	10. 30 x 37	11. 31 x 37	12. 33 x 37
13. 35 x 37	14. 37 x 37	15. 39 x 37	16. 32 x 37
17. 34 x 37	18. 36 x 37	19. 38 x 37	20. 40 x 37

EXERCISE M45

1. 41 x 37	2. 43 x 37	3. 45 x 37	4. 47 x 37
5. 49 x 37	6. 42 x 37	7. 44 x 37	8. 46 x 37
9. 48 x 37	10. 50 x 37	11. 51 x 37	12. 53 x 37
13. 55 x 37	14. 57 x 37	15. 59 x 37	16. 52 x 37
17. 54 x 37	18. 56 x 37	19. 58 x 37	20. 60 x 37

EXERCISE M46

1. 61 x 37 = ____

2. 63 x 37 = ____

3. 65 x 37 = ____

4. 67 x 37 = ____

5. 69 x 37 = ____

6. 62 x 37 = ____

7. 64 x 37 = ____

8. 66 x 37 = ____

9. 68 x 37 = ____

10. 70 x 37 = ____

11. 71 x 37 = ____

12. 73 x 37 = ____

13. 75 x 37 = ____

14. 77 x 37 = ____

15. 79 x 37 = ____

16. 72 x 37 = ____

17. 74 x 37 = ____

18. 76 x 37 = ____

19. 78 x 37 = ____

20. 8.0 x 37 = ____

EXERCISE M47

1. $\begin{array}{r} 81 \\ \times 37 \\ \hline \end{array}$

2. $\begin{array}{r} 83 \\ \times 37 \\ \hline \end{array}$

3. $\begin{array}{r} 85 \\ \times 37 \\ \hline \end{array}$

4. $\begin{array}{r} 87 \\ \times 37 \\ \hline \end{array}$

5. $\begin{array}{r} 89 \\ \times 37 \\ \hline \end{array}$

6. $\begin{array}{r} 82 \\ \times 37 \\ \hline \end{array}$

7. $\begin{array}{r} 84 \\ \times 37 \\ \hline \end{array}$

8. $\begin{array}{r} 86 \\ \times 37 \\ \hline \end{array}$

9. $\begin{array}{r} 88 \\ \times 37 \\ \hline \end{array}$

10. $\begin{array}{r} 90 \\ \times 37 \\ \hline \end{array}$

11. $\begin{array}{r} 91 \\ \times 37 \\ \hline \end{array}$

12. $\begin{array}{r} 93 \\ \times 37 \\ \hline \end{array}$

13. $\begin{array}{r} 95 \\ \times 37 \\ \hline \end{array}$

14. $\begin{array}{r} 97 \\ \times 37 \\ \hline \end{array}$

15. $\begin{array}{r} 99 \\ \times 37 \\ \hline \end{array}$

16. $\begin{array}{r} 92 \\ \times 37 \\ \hline \end{array}$

17. $\begin{array}{r} 94 \\ \times 37 \\ \hline \end{array}$

18. $\begin{array}{r} 96 \\ \times 37 \\ \hline \end{array}$

19. $\begin{array}{r} 98 \\ \times 37 \\ \hline \end{array}$

20. $\begin{array}{r} 100 \\ \times 37 \\ \hline \end{array}$

EXERCISE M48

1. 21 x 48	2. 23 x 48	3. 25 x 48	4. 27 x 48
5. 29 x 48	6. 22 x 48	7. 24 x 48	8. 26 x 48
9. 28 x 48	10. 30 x 48	11. 31 x 48	12. 33 x 48
13. 35 x 48	14. 37 x 48	15. 39 x 48	16. 32 x 48
17. 34 x 48	18. 36 x 48	19. 38 x 48	20. 40 x 48

EXERCISE M49

1. $\begin{array}{r} 41 \\ \times 48 \\ \hline \end{array}$	2. $\begin{array}{r} 43 \\ \times 48 \\ \hline \end{array}$	3. $\begin{array}{r} 45 \\ \times 48 \\ \hline \end{array}$	4. $\begin{array}{r} 47 \\ \times 48 \\ \hline \end{array}$
5. $\begin{array}{r} 49 \\ \times 48 \\ \hline \end{array}$	6. $\begin{array}{r} 42 \\ \times 48 \\ \hline \end{array}$	7. $\begin{array}{r} 44 \\ \times 48 \\ \hline \end{array}$	8. $\begin{array}{r} 46 \\ \times 48 \\ \hline \end{array}$
9. $\begin{array}{r} 48 \\ \times 48 \\ \hline \end{array}$	10. $\begin{array}{r} 50 \\ \times 48 \\ \hline \end{array}$	11. $\begin{array}{r} 51 \\ \times 48 \\ \hline \end{array}$	12. $\begin{array}{r} 53 \\ \times 48 \\ \hline \end{array}$
13. $\begin{array}{r} 55 \\ \times 48 \\ \hline \end{array}$	14. $\begin{array}{r} 57 \\ \times 48 \\ \hline \end{array}$	15. $\begin{array}{r} 59 \\ \times 48 \\ \hline \end{array}$	16. $\begin{array}{r} 52 \\ \times 48 \\ \hline \end{array}$
17. $\begin{array}{r} 54 \\ \times 48 \\ \hline \end{array}$	18. $\begin{array}{r} 56 \\ \times 48 \\ \hline \end{array}$	19. $\begin{array}{r} 58 \\ \times 48 \\ \hline \end{array}$	20. $\begin{array}{r} 60 \\ \times 48 \\ \hline \end{array}$

EXERCISE M50

1. 61 x 48	2. 63 x 48	3. 65 x 48	4. 67 x 48
5. 69 x 48	6. 62 x 48	7. 64 x 48	8. 66 x 48
9. 68 x 48	10. 70 x 48	11. 71 x 48	12. 73 x 48
13. 75 x 48	14. 77 x 48	15. 79 x 48	16. 72 x 48
17. 74 x 48	18. 76 x 48	19. 78 x 48	20. 80 x 48

EXERCISE M51

1. 81 x 48	2. 83 x 48	3. 85 x 48	4. 87 x 48
5. 89 x 48	6. 82 x 48	7. 84 x 48	8. 86 x 48
9. 88 x 48	10. 90 x 48	11. 91 x 48	12. 93 x 48
13. 95 x 48	14. 97 x 48	15. 99 x 48	16. 92 x 48
17. 94 x 48	18. 96 x 48	19. 98 x 48	20. 100 x 48

EXERCISE M52

1. 21 x 59	2. 23 x 59	3. 25 x 59	4. 27 x 59
5. 29 x 59	6. 22 x 59	7. 24 x 59	8. 26 x 59
9. 28 x 59	10. 30 x 59	11. 31 x 59	12. 33 x 59
13. 35 x 59	14. 37 x 59	15. 39 x 59	16. 32 x 59
17. 34 x 59	18. 36 x 59	19. 38 x 59	20. 40 x 59

EXERCISE M53

1. 41×59	2. 43×59	3. 45×59	4. 47×59
5. 49×59	6. 42×59	7. 44×59	8. 46×59
9. 48×59	10. 50×59	11. 51×59	12. 53×59
13. 55×59	14. 57×59	15. 59×59	16. 52×59
17. 54×59	18. 56×59	19. 58×59	20. 60×59

EXERCISE M54

1. 61×59	2. 63×59	3. 65×59	4. 67×59
5. 69×59	6. 62×59	7. 64×59	8. 66×59
9. 68×59	10. 70×59	11. 71×59	12. 73×59
13. 75×59	14. 77×59	15. 79×59	16. 72×59
17. 74×59	18. 76×59	19. 78×59	20. 80×59

EXERCISE M55

1. 81 x 59	2. 83 x 59	3. 85 x 59	4. 87 x 59
5. 89 x 59	6. 82 x 59	7. 84 x 59	8. 86 x 59
9. 88 x 59	10. 90 x 59	11. 91 x 59	12. 93 x 59
13. 95 x 59	14. 97 x 59	15. 99 x 59	16. 92 x 59
17. 94 x 59	18. 96 x 59	19. 98 x 59	20. 100 x 59

EXERCISE M56

1. $\begin{array}{r} 21 \\ \times 62 \\ \hline \end{array}$	2. $\begin{array}{r} 23 \\ \times 62 \\ \hline \end{array}$	3. $\begin{array}{r} 25 \\ \times 62 \\ \hline \end{array}$	4. $\begin{array}{r} 27 \\ \times 62 \\ \hline \end{array}$
5. $\begin{array}{r} 29 \\ \times 62 \\ \hline \end{array}$	6. $\begin{array}{r} 22 \\ \times 62 \\ \hline \end{array}$	7. $\begin{array}{r} 24 \\ \times 62 \\ \hline \end{array}$	8. $\begin{array}{r} 26 \\ \times 62 \\ \hline \end{array}$
9. $\begin{array}{r} 28 \\ \times 62 \\ \hline \end{array}$	10. $\begin{array}{r} 30 \\ \times 62 \\ \hline \end{array}$	11. $\begin{array}{r} 31 \\ \times 62 \\ \hline \end{array}$	12. $\begin{array}{r} 33 \\ \times 62 \\ \hline \end{array}$
13. $\begin{array}{r} 35 \\ \times 62 \\ \hline \end{array}$	14. $\begin{array}{r} 37 \\ \times 62 \\ \hline \end{array}$	15. $\begin{array}{r} 39 \\ \times 62 \\ \hline \end{array}$	16. $\begin{array}{r} 32 \\ \times 62 \\ \hline \end{array}$
17. $\begin{array}{r} 34 \\ \times 62 \\ \hline \end{array}$	18. $\begin{array}{r} 36 \\ \times 62 \\ \hline \end{array}$	19. $\begin{array}{r} 38 \\ \times 62 \\ \hline \end{array}$	20. $\begin{array}{r} 40 \\ \times 62 \\ \hline \end{array}$

EXERCISE M57

1. 41 x 62	2. 43 x 62	3. 45 x 62	4. 47 x 62
5. 49 x 62	6. 42 x 62	7. 44 x 62	8. 46 x 62
9. 48 x 62	10. 50 x 62	11. 51 x 62	12. 53 x 62
13. 55 x 62	14. 57 x 62	15. 59 x 62	16. 52 x 62
17. 54 x 62	18. 56 x 62	19. 58 x 62	20. 60 x 62

EXERCISE M58

1. 61 x 62

2. 63 x 62

3. 65 x 62

4. 67 x 62

5. 69 x 62

6. 62 x 62

7. 64 x 62

8. 66 x 62

9. 68 x 62

10. 70 x 62

11. 71 x 62

12. 73 x 62

13. 75 x 62

14. 77 x 62

15. 79 x 62

16. 72 x 62

17. 74 x 62

18. 76 x 62

19. 78 x 62

20. 8.0 x 62

EXERCISE M59

1. 81 x 62	2. 83 x 62	3. 85 x 62	4. 87 x 62
5. 89 x 62	6. 82 x 62	7. 84 x 62	8. 86 x 62
9. 88 x 62	10. 90 x 62	11. 91 x 62	12. 93 x 62
13. 95 x 62	14. 97 x 62	15. 99 x 62	16. 92 x 62
17. 94 x 62	18. 96 x 62	19. 98 x 62	20. 100 x 62

EXERCISE M60

1. $\begin{array}{r} 21 \\ \times 73 \\ \hline \end{array}$	2. $\begin{array}{r} 23 \\ \times 73 \\ \hline \end{array}$	3. $\begin{array}{r} 25 \\ \times 73 \\ \hline \end{array}$	4. $\begin{array}{r} 27 \\ \times 73 \\ \hline \end{array}$
5. $\begin{array}{r} 29 \\ \times 73 \\ \hline \end{array}$	6. $\begin{array}{r} 22 \\ \times 73 \\ \hline \end{array}$	7. $\begin{array}{r} 24 \\ \times 73 \\ \hline \end{array}$	8. $\begin{array}{r} 26 \\ \times 73 \\ \hline \end{array}$
9. $\begin{array}{r} 28 \\ \times 73 \\ \hline \end{array}$	10. $\begin{array}{r} 30 \\ \times 73 \\ \hline \end{array}$	11. $\begin{array}{r} 31 \\ \times 73 \\ \hline \end{array}$	12. $\begin{array}{r} 33 \\ \times 73 \\ \hline \end{array}$
13. $\begin{array}{r} 35 \\ \times 73 \\ \hline \end{array}$	14. $\begin{array}{r} 37 \\ \times 73 \\ \hline \end{array}$	15. $\begin{array}{r} 39 \\ \times 73 \\ \hline \end{array}$	16. $\begin{array}{r} 32 \\ \times 73 \\ \hline \end{array}$
17. $\begin{array}{r} 34 \\ \times 73 \\ \hline \end{array}$	18. $\begin{array}{r} 36 \\ \times 73 \\ \hline \end{array}$	19. $\begin{array}{r} 38 \\ \times 73 \\ \hline \end{array}$	20. $\begin{array}{r} 40 \\ \times 73 \\ \hline \end{array}$

EXERCISE M61

1. $\begin{array}{r} 41 \\ \times 73 \\ \hline \end{array}$	2. $\begin{array}{r} 43 \\ \times 73 \\ \hline \end{array}$	3. $\begin{array}{r} 45 \\ \times 73 \\ \hline \end{array}$	4. $\begin{array}{r} 47 \\ \times 73 \\ \hline \end{array}$
5. $\begin{array}{r} 49 \\ \times 73 \\ \hline \end{array}$	6. $\begin{array}{r} 42 \\ \times 73 \\ \hline \end{array}$	7. $\begin{array}{r} 44 \\ \times 73 \\ \hline \end{array}$	8. $\begin{array}{r} 46 \\ \times 73 \\ \hline \end{array}$
9. $\begin{array}{r} 48 \\ \times 73 \\ \hline \end{array}$	10. $\begin{array}{r} 50 \\ \times 73 \\ \hline \end{array}$	11. $\begin{array}{r} 51 \\ \times 73 \\ \hline \end{array}$	12. $\begin{array}{r} 53 \\ \times 73 \\ \hline \end{array}$
13. $\begin{array}{r} 55 \\ \times 73 \\ \hline \end{array}$	14. $\begin{array}{r} 57 \\ \times 73 \\ \hline \end{array}$	15. $\begin{array}{r} 59 \\ \times 73 \\ \hline \end{array}$	16. $\begin{array}{r} 52 \\ \times 73 \\ \hline \end{array}$
17. $\begin{array}{r} 54 \\ \times 73 \\ \hline \end{array}$	18. $\begin{array}{r} 56 \\ \times 73 \\ \hline \end{array}$	19. $\begin{array}{r} 58 \\ \times 73 \\ \hline \end{array}$	20. $\begin{array}{r} 60 \\ \times 73 \\ \hline \end{array}$

EXERCISE M62

1. 61×73	2. 63×73	3. 65×73	4. 67×73
5. 69×73	6. 62×73	7. 64×73	8. 66×73
9. 68×73	10. 70×73	11. 71×73	12. 73×73
13. 75×73	14. 77×73	15. 79×73	16. 72×73
17. 74×73	18. 76×73	19. 78×73	20. 80×73

EXERCISE M63

1. $\begin{array}{r} 81 \\ \times 73 \\ \hline \end{array}$

2. $\begin{array}{r} 83 \\ \times 73 \\ \hline \end{array}$

3. $\begin{array}{r} 85 \\ \times 73 \\ \hline \end{array}$

4. $\begin{array}{r} 87 \\ \times 73 \\ \hline \end{array}$

5. $\begin{array}{r} 89 \\ \times 73 \\ \hline \end{array}$

6. $\begin{array}{r} 82 \\ \times 73 \\ \hline \end{array}$

7. $\begin{array}{r} 84 \\ \times 73 \\ \hline \end{array}$

8. $\begin{array}{r} 86 \\ \times 73 \\ \hline \end{array}$

9. $\begin{array}{r} 88 \\ \times 73 \\ \hline \end{array}$

10. $\begin{array}{r} 90 \\ \times 73 \\ \hline \end{array}$

11. $\begin{array}{r} 91 \\ \times 73 \\ \hline \end{array}$

12. $\begin{array}{r} 93 \\ \times 73 \\ \hline \end{array}$

13. $\begin{array}{r} 95 \\ \times 73 \\ \hline \end{array}$

14. $\begin{array}{r} 97 \\ \times 73 \\ \hline \end{array}$

15. $\begin{array}{r} 99 \\ \times 73 \\ \hline \end{array}$

16. $\begin{array}{r} 92 \\ \times 73 \\ \hline \end{array}$

17. $\begin{array}{r} 94 \\ \times 73 \\ \hline \end{array}$

18. $\begin{array}{r} 96 \\ \times 73 \\ \hline \end{array}$

19. $\begin{array}{r} 98 \\ \times 73 \\ \hline \end{array}$

20. $\begin{array}{r} 100 \\ \times 73 \\ \hline \end{array}$

EXERCISE M64

1. 21 x 84	2. 23 x 84	3. 25 x 84	4. 27 x 84
5. 29 x 84	6. 22 x 84	7. 24 x 84	8. 26 x 84
9. 28 x 84	10. 30 x 84	11. 31 x 84	12. 33 x 84
13. 35 x 84	14. 37 x 84	15. 39 x 84	16. 32 x 84
17. 34 x 84	18. 36 x 84	19. 38 x 84	20. 40 x 84

EXERCISE M65

1. 41 x 84	2. 43 x 84	3. 45 x 84	4. 47 x 84
5. 49 x 84	6. 42 x 84	7. 44 x 84	8. 46 x 84
9. 48 x 84	10. 50 x 84	11. 51 x 84	12. 53 x 84
13. 55 x 84	14. 57 x 84	15. 59 x 84	16. 52 x 84
17. 54 x 84	18. 56 x 84	19. 58 x 84	20. 60 x 84

EXERCISE M66

1. 61 x 84	2. 63 x 84	3. 65 x 84	4. 67 x 84
5. 69 x 84	6. 62 x 84	7. 64 x 84	8. 66 x 84
9. 68 x 84	10. 70 x 84	11. 71 x 84	12. 73 x 84
13. 7.5 x 84	14. 77 x 84	15. 79 x 84	16. 72 x 84
17. 74 x 84	18. 76 x 84	19. 78 x 84	20. 80 x 84

EXERCISE M67

1. 81 x 84	2. 83 x 84	3. 85 x 84	4. 87 x 84
5. 89 x 84	6. 82 x 84	7. 84 x 84	8. 86 x 84
9. 88 x 84	10. 90 x 84	11. 91 x 84	12. 93 x 84
13. 9.5 x 84	14. 97 x 84	15. 99 x 84	16. 92 x 84
17. 94 x 84	18. 96 x 84	19. 98 x 84	20. 100 x 84

EXERCISE M68

1. 21 x 95	2. 23 x 95	3. 25 x 95	4. 27 x 95
5. 29 x 95	6. 22 x 95	7. 24 x 95	8. 26 x 95
9. 28 x 95	10. 30 x 95	11. 31 x 95	12. 33 x 95
13. 35 x 95	14. 37 x 95	15. 39 x 95	16. 32 x 95
17. 34 x 95	18. 36 x 95	19. 38 x 95	20. 40 x 95

EXERCISE M69

1. 41 x 95

2. 43 x 95

3. 45 x 95

4. 47 x 95

5. 49 x 95

6. 42 x 95

7. 44 x 95

8. 46 x 95

9. 48 x 95

10. 50 x 95

11. 51 x 95

12. 53 x 95

13. 55 x 95

14. 57 x 95

15. 59 x 95

16. 52 x 95

17. 54 x 95

18. 56 x 95

19. 58 x 95

20. 60 x 95

EXERCISE M70

1. 123 x 12	2. 146 x 12	3. 157 x 12	4. 169 x 12
5. 126 x 13	6. 134 x 13	7. 159 x 13	8. 168 x 13
9. 137 x 14	10. 146 x 14	11. 158 x 14	12. 189 x 14
13. 148 x 15	14. 157 x 15	15. 168 x 15	16. 179 x 15
17. 149 x 12	18. 139 x 13	19. 167 x 14	20. 184 x 15

EXERCISE M71

1. 149 x16	2. 158 x16	3. 189 x16	4. 195 x16
5. 156 x17	6. 163 x17	7. 178 x17	8. 189 x17
9. 179 x18	10. 185 x18	11. 192 x18	12. 198 x18
13. 187 x19	14. 189 x19	15. 193 x19	16. 199 x19
17. 163 x16	18. 194 x17	19. 196 x18	20. 197 x19

EXERCISE M72

1. 236 x 12	2. 259 x 12	3. 268 x 12	4. 279 x 12
5. 247 x 13	6. 269 x 13	7. 275 x 13	8. 298 x 13
9. 258 x 14	10. 278 x 14	11. 289 x 14	12. 299 x 14
13. 265 x 15	14. 248 x 15	15. 283 x 15	16. 297 x 15
17. 248 x 12	18. 287 x 13	19. 269 x 14	20. 259 x 15

EXERCISE M73

1. 278 x 16	2. 285 x 16	3. 291 x 16	4. 298 x 16
5. 267 x 17	6. 276 x 17	7. 269 x 17	8. 297 x 17
9. 287 x 18	10. 294 x 18	11. 296 x 18	12. 298 x 18
13. 284 x 19	14. 289 x 19	15. 297 x 19	16. 299 x 19
17. 269 x 16	18. 287 x 17	19. 275 x 18	20. 279 x 19

EXERCISE M74

1. 346 x 12

2. 357 x 12

3. 386 x 12

4. 397 x 12

5. 374 x 13

6. 386 x 13

7. 392 x 13

8. 399 x 13

9. 384 x 14

10. 387 x 14

11. 394 x 14

12. 398 x 14

13. 386 x 15

14. 388 x 15

15. 395 x 15

16. 399 x 15

17. 329 x 12

18. 369 x 13

19. 379 x 14

20. 379 x 15

EXERCISE M75

1. 426 x 16	2. 438 x 16	3. 456 x 16	4. 467 x 16
5. 473 x 17	6. 484 x 17	7. 496 x 17	8. 498 x 17
9. 526 x 18	10. 547 x 18	11. 569 x 18	12. 578 x 18
13. 645 x 19	14. 673 x 19	15. 685 x 19	16. 698 x 19
17. 489 x 16	18. 456 x 17	19. 589 x 18	20. 659 x 19

EXERCISE M76

1. 734 x 12	2. 746 x 12	3. 759 x 12	4. 785 x 12
5. 846 x 13	6. 857 x 13	7. 869 x 13	8. 879 x 13
9. 887 x 14	10. 899 x 14	11. 946 x 14	12. 957 x 14
13. 964 x 15	14. 976 x 15	15. 987 x 15	16. 998 x 15
17. 764 x 12	18. 897 x 13	19. 978 x 14	20. 957 x 15

EXERCISE M77

1. 746 x 16	2. 859 x 16	3. 867 x 16	4. 986 x 16
5. 889 x 17	6. 897 x 17	7. 899 x 17	8. 946 x 17
9. 894 x 18	10. 899 x 18	11. 946 x 18	12. 968 x 18
13. 946 x 19	14. 957 x 19	15. 968 x 19	16. 987 x 19
17. 798 x 16	18. 875 x 17	19. 936 x 18	20. 974 x 19

EXERCISE M78

1. 246 x 23	2. 357 x 25	3. 568 x 27	4. 786 x 29
5. 354 x 34	6. 578 x 36	7. 768 x 38	8. 974 x 39
9. 475 x 42	10. 684 x 46	11. 879 x 48	12. 965 x 49
13. 567 x 53	14. 675 x 55	15. 886 x 57	16. 896 x 59
17. 468 x 32	18. 694 x 37	19. 486 x 45	20. 769 x 56

EXERCISE M79

1. 623 x 62
2. 678 x 65
3. 686 x 67
4. 797 x 69
5. 826 x 73
6. 837 x 75
7. 936 x 77
8. 948 x 79
9. 952 x 84
10. 967 x 86
11. 974 x 88
12. 984 x 89
13. 937 x 92
14. 956 x 95
15. 978 x 87
16. 999 x 99
17. 657 x 63
18. 859 x 72
19. 978 x 89
20. 947 x 93

EXERCISE M80

1. 207 x 13	2. 309 x 15	3. 506 x 17	4. 403 x 19
5. 304 x 23	6. 408 x 26	7. 607 x 28	8. 809 x 29
9. 406 x 33	10. 508 x 35	11. 609 x 37	12. 706 x 39
13. 507 x 48	14. 606 x 46	15. 808 x 47	16. 903 x 49
17. 409 x 18	18. 503 x 27	19. 709 x 37	20. 708 x 45

EXERCISE M81

1. 605 x52	2. 607 x54	3. 708 x56	4. 809 x58
5. 608 x63	6. 705 x67	7. 803 x68	8. 809 x69
9. 706 x72	10. 805 x73	11. 809 x77	12. 902 x74
13. 707 x83	14. 806 x85	15. 905 x87	16. 909 x89
17. 807 x57	18. 709 x65	19. 804 x79	20. 906 x86

EXERCISE M82

1. 260 x 13	2. 370 x 15	3. 460 x 17	4. 570 x 18
5. 350 x 24	6. 480 x 26	7. 760 x 28	8. 870 x 29
9. 470 x 34	10. 570 x 36	11. 790 x 37	12. 980 x 39
13. 530 x 43	14. 640 x 45	15. 750 x 47	16. 870 x 49
17. 270 x 16	18. 530 x 27	19. 650 x 35	20. 980 x 42

EXERCISE M83

1. 650 x 52	2. 670 x 54	3. 680 x 57	4. 890 x 58
5. 690 x 64	6. 630 x 68	7. 870 x 67	8. 930 x 69
9. 710 x 73	10. 740 x 75	11. 750 x 76	12. 780 x 78
13. 730 x 82	14. 750 x 85	15. 770 x 87	16. 790 x 89
17. 720 x 55	18. 670 x 62	19. 760 x 74	20. 870 x 86

EXERCISE M84

1. 1468 x 178

2. 1687 x 197

3. 1768 x 216

4. 1968 x 237

5. 2764 x 349

6. 2909 x 364

7. 3216 x 437

8. 4307 x 457

9. 5564 x 518

10. 5590 x 586

11. 5870 x 634

12. 5900 x 709

13. 6500 x 640

14. 7360 x 604

15. 9200 x 637

EXERCISE M85

1. 6734
   x760

2. 7206
   x792

3. 7359
   x863

4. 7602
   x891

5. 7842
   x912

6. 7900
   x904

7. 8006
   x940

8. 8210
   x951

9. 8357
   x976

10. 8407
    x908

11. 8609
    x914

12. 8726
    x926

13. 6042
    x637

14. 7046
    x427

15. 7045
    x563

EXERCISE M86

1. 409 x 36
2. 806 x 53
3. 298 x 97
4. 36 x 408
5. 840 x 87
6. 56 x 17
7. 510 x 47
8. 794 x 56
9. 468 x 57
10. 72 x 890
11. 6 x 42607
12. 18 x 2009

EXERCISE M87

1. 64 x 729
2. 89 x 924
3. 39 x 864
4. 81 x 3489
5. 48 x 5278
6. 29 x 6003
7. 2069 x 18
8. 63 x 94
9. 43 x 706
10. 846 x 6849
11. 59 x 637
12. 605 x 7060

EXERCISE M88

1. 1657 x 14	2. 1364 x 16	3. 2473 x 18
4. 2627 x 19	5. 3248 x 23	6. 3307 x 25
7. 4008 x 27	8. 4219 x 28	9. 4348 x 32
10. 4826 x 34	11. 4809 x 36	12. 4098 x 39
13. 6407 x 42	14. 7340 x 47	15. 8096 x 49

EXERCISE M89

1. 5009 x 41	2. 5219 x 43	3. 5789 x 45
4. 5909 x 48	5. 6086 x 52	6. 6005 x 55
7. 6897 x 57	8. 7010 x 59	9. 8012 x 62
10. 8536 x 65	11. 8706 x 67	12. 9090 x 68
13. 4007 x 73	14. 7604 x 75	15. 7410 x 78

EXERCISE M90

1. 7086 x72	2. 8009 x74	3. 7304 x76
4. 6468 x79	5. 7346 x83	6. 9098 x85
7. 8908 x87	8. 9069 x88	9. 8899 x91
10. 9600 x93	11. 8403 x95	12. 9002 x97
13. 6040 x78	14. 6798 x84	15. 9100 x96

EXERCISE M91

1. $\begin{array}{r} 256 \\ \times 123 \\ \hline \end{array}$

2. $\begin{array}{r} 278 \\ \times 145 \\ \hline \end{array}$

3. $\begin{array}{r} 296 \\ \times 157 \\ \hline \end{array}$

4. $\begin{array}{r} 306 \\ \times 168 \\ \hline \end{array}$

5. $\begin{array}{r} 346 \\ \times 186 \\ \hline \end{array}$

6. $\begin{array}{r} 357 \\ \times 198 \\ \hline \end{array}$

7. $\begin{array}{r} 368 \\ \times 246 \\ \hline \end{array}$

8. $\begin{array}{r} 379 \\ \times 270 \\ \hline \end{array}$

9. $\begin{array}{r} 390 \\ \times 287 \\ \hline \end{array}$

10. $\begin{array}{r} 428 \\ \times 326 \\ \hline \end{array}$

11. $\begin{array}{r} 456 \\ \times 347 \\ \hline \end{array}$

12. $\begin{array}{r} 478 \\ \times 369 \\ \hline \end{array}$

13. $\begin{array}{r} 489 \\ \times 372 \\ \hline \end{array}$

14. $\begin{array}{r} 530 \\ \times 378 \\ \hline \end{array}$

15. $\begin{array}{r} 540 \\ \times 382 \\ \hline \end{array}$

EXERCISE M92

1. $\begin{array}{r} 520 \\ \times 374 \\ \hline \end{array}$

2. $\begin{array}{r} 537 \\ \times 386 \\ \hline \end{array}$

3. $\begin{array}{r} 567 \\ \times 399 \\ \hline \end{array}$

4. $\begin{array}{r} 509 \\ \times 406 \\ \hline \end{array}$

5. $\begin{array}{r} 638 \\ \times 436 \\ \hline \end{array}$

6. $\begin{array}{r} 674 \\ \times 450 \\ \hline \end{array}$

7. $\begin{array}{r} 690 \\ \times 472 \\ \hline \end{array}$

8. $\begin{array}{r} 708 \\ \times 586 \\ \hline \end{array}$

9. $\begin{array}{r} 749 \\ \times 679 \\ \hline \end{array}$

10. $\begin{array}{r} 780 \\ \times 690 \\ \hline \end{array}$

11. $\begin{array}{r} 826 \\ \times 706 \\ \hline \end{array}$

12. $\begin{array}{r} 846 \\ \times 780 \\ \hline \end{array}$

13. $\begin{array}{r} 859 \\ \times 852 \\ \hline \end{array}$

14. $\begin{array}{r} 897 \\ \times 865 \\ \hline \end{array}$

15. $\begin{array}{r} 986 \\ \times 957 \\ \hline \end{array}$

EXERCISE M93

1. Four threes.
2. Six fives.
3. Seven times two pence.
4. Eight threes.
5. Eleven times one.
6. How many sweets are there in three bags of five sweets.
7. Nine fours.
8. Seven multiplied by three.
9. Seven multiplied by nine.
10. Ten multiplied by four.
11. Four times five pounds.
12. What is the cost of four bars of chocolate which are twenty pence each?
13. Eleven threes.
14. What is the cost of four three pence lollipops?
15. If I cut twelve flowers to put into one vase, how many would I need for two vases?
16. Five multiplied by four.

EXERCISE M94

1. A bag of chips costs 15p. What is the cost of 2 bags?

2. I need 3 eggs to make a cake. How many will I need to make 5 cakes?

3. Every day my mother walks 3 km. How far does she walk in 7 days?

4. The milkman leaves me 2 pints of milk a day. How much is that in 1 week (7 days)?

5. I can buy potatoes for 9p for ½ kg. How much will that cost me for 1 kg?

6. Dress material costs £2 a metre. My school dress needs 3 metres. How much will it cost?

7. Fish and chips cost 80p. How much shall I have to pay for 3 portions?

EXERCISE M95

1. 3 children each have 2 apples. How many apples are there altogether?

2. 4 families each have 3 children. How many children are there?

3. A bag of sweets costs ten pence. What would be the cost of 6 bags?

4. A class has 20 pupils. How many feet do they have altogether?

5. My father has 3 horses. How many horse shoes will they need?

6. In a class of 20, every pupil must have 5 books. How many books are needed?

7. My bus fare to school is 12p a day. How much do I need for 5 days?

EXERCISE M96

Copy these tables into your book, and fill in the missing numbers:

Multiply and divide by 2

1 x 2 = 2	2 ÷ 2 = 1
2 x 2 = 4	4 ÷ 2 = 2
3 x 2 = □	□ ÷ 2 = 3
4 x 2 = 8	□ ÷ 2 = 4
5 x 2 = □	10 ÷ 2 = □
6 x 2 = 12	12 ÷ □ = 6
7 x 2 = □	□ ÷ 2 = 7
8 x 2 = 16	16 ÷ □ = 8
9 x 2 = □	18 ÷ □ = 9
10 x 2 = 20	20 ÷ 2 = □
11 x 2 = 22	□ ÷ 2 = 11
12 x 2 = □	24 ÷ □ = 12

Multiply and divide by 3

1 x 3 = 3	3 ÷ 3 = 1
2 x 3 = 6	6 ÷ 3 = □
3 x 3 = □	9 ÷ 3 = □
4 x 3 = 12	12 ÷ 3 = □
5 x 3 = □	□ ÷ 3 = 5
6 x 3 = 18	18 ÷ 3 = □
7 x 3 = 21	21 ÷ □ = 7
8 x 3 = □	□ ÷ 3 = 8
9 x 3 = 27	27 ÷ 3 = □
10 x 3 = □	30 ÷ □ = 10
11 x 3 = 33	□ ÷ 3 = 11
12 x 3 = 36	36 ÷ 3 = 12

EXERCISE M97

Copy these tables into your book, and fill in the missing numbers:

Multiply and divide by 4

1 x 4 = 4	4 ÷ 4 = 1
2 x 4 = □	8 ÷ □ = 2
3 x 4 = 12	12 ÷ 4 = □
4 x 4 = 16	16 ÷ □ = 4
5 x 4 = □	□ ÷ 4 = 5
6 x 4 = 24	24 ÷ 4 = □
7 x □ = 28	28 ÷ □ = 7
8 x 4 = □	32 ÷ 4 = □
9 x 4 = 36	□ ÷ 4 = 9
10 x □ = 40	□ ÷ 4 = 10
11 x 4 = □	44 ÷ 4 = □
12 x 4 = 48	48 ÷ 4 = 12

Multiply and divide by 5

1 x 5 = 5	5 ÷ 5 = □
2 x 5 = □	10 ÷ □ = 2
3 x □ = 15	15 ÷ 5 = 3
4 x 5 = □	□ ÷ 5 = 4
5 x 5 = 25	25 ÷ 5 = □
6 x □ = 30	30 ÷ □ = 6
7 x 5 = 35	35 ÷ 5 = □
8 x □ = 40	□ ÷ 5 = 8
9 x 5 = 45	□ ÷ 5 = 9
10 x 5 = □	50 ÷ 5 = □
11 x □ = 55	□ ÷ 5 = 11
12 x 5 = 60	60 ÷ 5 = □

EXERCISE M98

Copy these tables into your book, and fill in the missing numbers:

Multiply and divide by 6

1 x 6 = 6	6 ÷ 6 = □
2 x 6 = □	12 ÷ □ = 2
3 x 6 = 18	18 ÷ 6 = □
4 x □ = 24	24 ÷ 6 = 4
5 x 6 = 30	30 ÷ □ = 5
6 x 6 = □	36 ÷ 6 = 6
7 x □ = 42	□ ÷ 6 = 7
8 x 6 = 48	48 ÷ 6 = □
9 x 6 = □	54 ÷ 6 = 9
10 x □ = 60	□ ÷ 6 = 10
11 x 6 = 66	66 ÷ 6 = □
12 x 6 = □	72 ÷ 6 = 12

Multiply and divide by 7

1 x 7 = □	7 ÷ 7 = 1
2 x 7 = 14	14 ÷ 7 = □
3 x 7 = 21	□ ÷ 7 = 3
4 x 7 = □	28 ÷ 7 = □
5 x 7 = 35	35 ÷ □ = 5
6 x □ = 42	42 ÷ 7 = 6
7 x 7 = □	49 ÷ 7 = □
8 x 7 = 56	□ ÷ 7 = 8
9 x 7 = 63	63 ÷ □ = 9
10 x 7 = □	70 ÷ 7 = □
11 x 7 = □	77 ÷ □ = 11
12 x 7 = 84	84 ÷ 7 = 12

EXERCISE M99

Copy these tables into your book, and fill in the missing numbers:

Multiply and divide by 8

1 x 8 = 8	8 ÷ 8 = 1
2 x 8 = □	16 ÷ 8 = □
3 x 8 = 24	24 ÷ 8 = □
4 x 8 = 32	32 ÷ 8 = □
5 x 8 = □	40 ÷ □ = 5
6 x 8 = 48	48 ÷ 8 = 6
7 x 8 = 56	56 ÷ 8 = □
8 x 8 = □	64 ÷ 8 = 8
9 x 8 = 72	72 ÷ 8 = 9
10 x 8 = □	80 ÷ 8 = □
11 x 8 = 88	88 ÷ □ = 11
12 x 8 = 96	96 ÷ 8 = 12

Multiply and divide by 9

1 x 9 = 9	9 ÷ 9 = 1
2 x 9 = □	18 ÷ □ = 2
3 x □ = 27	27 ÷ 9 = 3
4 x 9 = 36	□ ÷ 9 = 4
5 x 9 = □	45 ÷ 9 = □
6 x 9 = 54	54 ÷ 9 = 6
7 x □ = 63	□ ÷ 9 = 7
8 x 9 = □	72 ÷ 9 = □
9 x □ = 81	81 ÷ 9 = □
10 x 9 = □	90 ÷ □ = 10
11 x 9 = □	99 ÷ 9 = □
12 x 9 = 108	108 ÷ 9 = 12

EXERCISE M100

Copy these tables into your book, and fill in the missing numbers:

Multiply and divide by 10

1 x 10 = 10	10 ÷ 10 = 1
2 x 10 = □	20 ÷ □ = 2
3 x 10 = □	30 ÷ □ = 3
4 x 10 = □	40 ÷ 10 = □
5 x □ = 50	50 ÷ 10 = □
6 x 10 = 60	60 ÷ □ = 6
7 x 10 = □	70 ÷ 10 = 7
8 x □ = 80	80 ÷ □ = 8
9 x 10 = 90	90 ÷ 10 = □
10 x 10 = □	100 ÷ 10 = □
11 x 10 = 110	110 ÷ 10 = 11
12 x 10 = □	120 ÷ 10 = 12

Multiply and divide by 11

1 x 11 = 11	11 ÷ 11 = □
2 x 11 = □	22 ÷ 11 = □
3 x 11 = 33	□ ÷ 11 = 3
4 x □ = 44	44 ÷ □ = 4
5 x □ = 55	55 ÷ 11 = 5
6 x 11 = □	66 ÷ □ = 6
7 x 11 = 77	□ ÷ 11 = 7
8 x □ = 88	88 ÷ 11 = □
9 x 11 = □	99 ÷ □ = 9
10 x 11 = 110	□ ÷ 11 = 10
11 x 11 = □	121 ÷ □ = 11
12 x 11 = 132	□ ÷ 11 = 12

EXERCISE M101

Copy this table into your book, and fill in the missing numbers:

Multiply and divide by 12

1 x 12 = □	12 ÷ 12 = 1
2 x 12 = 24	□ ÷ 12 = 2
3 x □ = 36	36 ÷ 12 = □
4 x 12 = □	48 ÷ □ = 4
5 x 12 = 60	□ ÷ 12 = 5
6 x 12 = □	72 ÷ 12 = □
7 x 12 = 84	84 ÷ □ = 7
8 x 12 = □	96 ÷ 12 = □
9 x 12 = 108	108 ÷ □ = 9
10 x □ = 120	120 ÷ 12 = □
11 x 12 = □	132 ÷ 12 = 11
12 x 12 = 144	144 ÷ □ = 12

EXERCISE M102

■	1	2		■
3	■		■	4
5		■	6	
	■	7	■	
■	8			■

ACROSS		DOWN	
1.	11 x 11	2.	5 x 5
5.	7 x 6	3.	12 x 12
6.	3 x 11	4.	12 x 11
8.	10 x 10	7.	4 x 20

EXERCISE M103

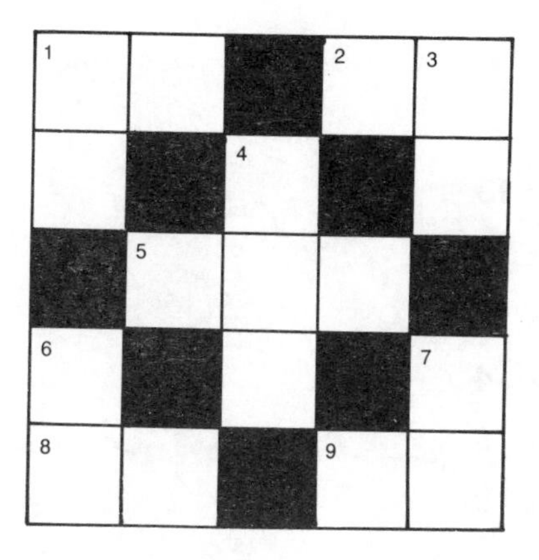

ACROSS		DOWN	
1.	7 x 12	1.	9 x 9
2.	9 x 7	3.	3 x 11
5.	12 x 10	4.	80 x 4
8.	6 x 8	6.	8 x 8
9.	2 x 13	7.	7 x 8

EXERCISE M104

ACROSS

1. **12 x 12**
4. **7 x 3**
6. **4 x 6**
8. **8 x 8**
9. **11 x 1**
10. **12 x 11**
13. **20 x 12**
15. **2 x 5**
16. **2 x 21**
17. **6 x 2**
20. **3 x 8**
21. **50 x 4**

DOWN

1. **2 x 7**
2. **4 x 10**
3. **112 x 2**
5. **11 x 11**
7. **9 x 7**
11. **5 x 5**
12. **4 x 13**
14. **6 x 8**
15. **61 x 2**
16. **105 x 4**
18. **4 x 8**
19. **6 x 5**

EXERCISE M105

ACROSS

1.	6 x 3
3.	3 x 13
5.	2 x 10
6.	111 x 3
9.	20 x 2
11.	21 x 3
12.	61 x 2
14.	111 x 4
16.	4 x 3
18.	2 x 13
19.	122 x 3
21.	11 x 2
22.	4 x 12
23.	2 x 21

DOWN

1.	4 x 30	13.	60 x 4
2.	20 x 4	15.	4 x 4
4.	31 x 3	16.	13 x 1
7.	4 x 9	17.	2 x 13
8.	3 x 11	18.	2 x 111
9.	11 x 4	20.	8 x 8
10.	112 x 2	21.	3 x 8

NOTES

NOTES

NOTES